# Jillian Jiggs
## and the
## Secret Surprise

### Phoebe Gilman

## Scholastic Canada Ltd.

Toronto New York London Auckland Sydney
Mexico City New Delhi Hong Kong Buenos Aires

The paintings for this book were created in gouache and coloured pencils
on Arches Watercolour Paper.

This book was designed in QuarkXPress, with type set in 16 point American Typewriter.

National Library of Canada Cataloguing in Publication Data

Gilman, Phoebe, 1940-
Jillian Jiggs and the secret surprise

ISBN 0-439-98970-1
Title.

PS8563.I54J54 2002          jC813'.54          C2001-902735-4
PZ83.G4218Jil 2002

7 6 5 4 3 2 1          Printed and bound in Canada          02 03 04 05 06

For the new kids
on the block

| Ariana | Emily | Matthew |
| Connor | Morgan | Griffin |
| Sammy | Jacob | Rachel |
| | Derian | |

The streamers flip-flapped in the soft, summer breeze.
Balloons bobbed and bounced on the branches of trees.
But Jillian sat on the steps feeling sad.
"Oh, I'm a bad sister. Oh, I'm bad bad bad.
I can't buy a present. I haven't a cent.
How did it happen? My money's all spent."

1

"Jillian Jiggs," Rachel said to her friend,
"Stop moaning and groaning. This isn't the end.
Take my advice, and make no mistake:
The best birthday present is one that you make."

"She's right," Peter said. "And I'm counting on you
To think up a present for me to give, too."

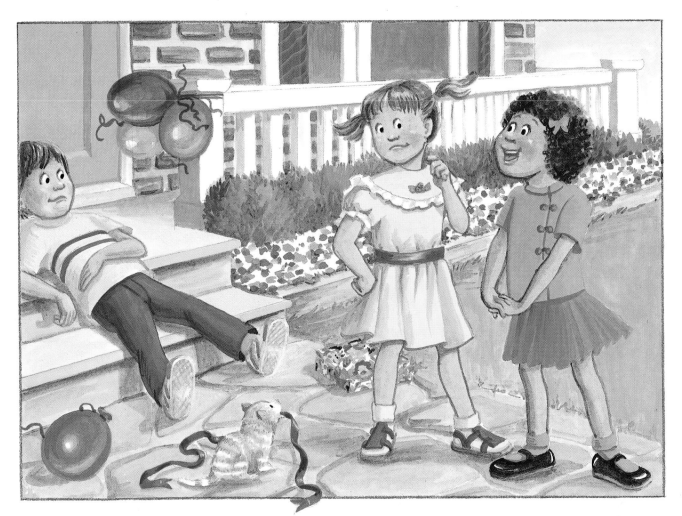

As Jillian listened, she nodded her head.
"You think I can do it? I'll do it!" she said.

"How about this? We could put on a show.
We'll plan it in secret. Rebecca won't know
What we are doing until it's all done."
"I like that," said Rachel. "Surprises are fun."

3

A few dabs of paint and a doodad or two
Made old clothes and boxes look magically new.
At last they were ready. Rehearsals began.
But things didn't happen according to plan.

For while they were busy rehearsing the show,
Nobody bothered to look out below.

They didn't see that Rebecca's friend Shirley
Had come to the party a little too early.

"I want to be in the birthday show, too.
I want to be a great actor like you."

"Oh, no!" Rachel said. "That's the end of our fun.
The surprise will be over before it's begun."

They looked at Shirley, then looked at each other.
And Shirley became the new Royal Queen Mother.

"Okay, now that's settled," Jillian said.
She hadn't noticed that Molly and Fred
Had watched Shirley put on her jewels and her crown.

"That isn't fair," Molly said and sat down.
"We want to be in the birthday show, too.
We want to be famous actors like you."

So Peter invented a dragon named Quizzle,
With scaly green spikes and a frightening sizzle.
But neither one would be the dragon's rear end.

"You would change places if you were my friend."

Jillian said, "There is no need to fight.
The beast has two heads. There is no end in sight."

They snorted and roared and breathed fiery breath.
They sizzled and fried and scared Peter to death.

"Okay. Now that's settled," Jillian said.
"On with the show!" and she nodded her head.

But nothing was settled. In fact, things got messy.
When she turned around – there was Sarah and Jesse.

"We want to be in the birthday show, too.
We want to be famous actors like you."

14

The cast just kept growing. It didn't take long
Before things began to go even more wrong.

"We want a part," Mark and Emily cried.
"It isn't fun to be shuffled aside."

15

"Please. Pretty please," Max and Natalie pleaded.
"There must be a small part where we would be needed."

Jillian told them they had to be quiet.
But they wouldn't listen. They started to riot.

16

"We want to be in the birthday show, too.
We want to be famous actors like you."

The guests wouldn't go to the party. They'd whine,
Or climb on the stage and say, "This side is fine."

17

Jillian said, "What a tough situation.
I'll need more parts than my first calculation."

Peter just shrugged and said, "Jillian Jiggs,
All this play needs is a chorus of pigs!"

"Yes!" the guests shouted. "Oink, oink, hooray!"

Jillian nodded. "Then on with the play!
Now we are ready. No more can be done."
That's when she heard the words . . .

19

"Where's everyone?"

"Oh, no! It's Rebecca. What'll I do?
She shouldn't see this until we are through."

"Jillian, Jillian, let me play, too."

"This isn't a game. It's my present for you."

"You say it's my present? Then hold on a minute. Today is MY birthday. I want to be in it."

And that's how Rebecca became the star mouse
Who led the whole cast to the back of the house.

There they fixed up a stage and got set to begin.
The curtains were opened. The chorus came in.
And then they stopped . . .

23

. . . because no one was there.
All that they saw was just chair after chair.

"What'll we do? What kind of a show
Has no one to watch it? We'd like to know!"

24

Jillian gulped and said, "Quick, close the curtain.
I've thought of someone, and I'm very certain
That SHE will not want to be part of the show.
She will be happy to sit down. I know.
Okay, everybody. Now, please, close your eyes.
I'm going to get the last birthday . . . "

# "SURPRISE!"

(This is the end, but if you want more,
Put on your own play. Bravo! Encore!
Want to know how? It's easy. Just look
At Jillian's play in the back of this book.)

# Jillian Jiggs

*Presents*

# The Chicken Princess

## *The Cast*
### in order of appearance:

**Queen**

**Hero**

**Chorus**
*(as many people as you like)*

**Dave the Giant**

**Mouse**

**Dragon**
*(with as many heads as you like)*

**Wizard**

**Princess**

If you have more actors they can appear, in a variety of costumes,
in the magic wand scene in Act 3.

For costume, prop and staging tips check out Phoebe Gilman's website: www.phoebegilman.com

# ACT I

## *The Queen's Castle*

**CHORUS**
A wild wind is blowing, OO WOO all around.
The trees are all frosted. Snow covers the ground.
The curtain is opened. Now let us begin.
Here is the castle. Queen Esther comes in.

*The curtain opens on the inside of a castle room.
There is a mop propped against the wall.*

**QUEEN**
Alas! Woe is me! That evil, mean Wizard
Has stolen the Princess away in the blizzard.

*The Hero enters.*

**HERO**
Forsooth! Never fear! And do not be sad.
I am the Hero and I'm really mad.
I am the Hero and I'll save the day.
That is the reason that I'm in this play.

**QUEEN**
Without my sweet child, life has no meaning.
Now I must go. The castle needs cleaning.

*She reaches for the mop.*

**QUEEN**
Oh, by the way, you know about Dave,
The rather large giant who watches the cave?

*The Hero shakes his head, looking worried.*

**QUEEN**
You don't? Now you do. Better take care.
Look out for Dave, when you get there.

*The Queen exits. The Hero speaks before
exiting too.*

**HERO**
Farewell! I am going out in the blizzard.
I'll rescue the Princess and capture the Wizard.

*The curtain closes. When it re-opens, we see a snowy
landscape with a cave. The Hero runs in place.*

**CHORUS**
*(makes wind sounds: Ooo wooo! Ooo woo! etc.)*

**HERO**
Brr. I am freezing. This cold wind doth blast.
I'm trying to run, but it's hard to move fast.

**CHORUS**
*(to the audience)*
Our Hero needs help. Can you stomp your feet,
As if you were running? But stay in your seat.

*The Hero runs faster in place.*

**HERO**
What's that I see there? A dark, gloomy cave.
I don't see the Wizard, and I don't see Dave.

**GIANT**
*(aside to the audience)*
Of course he won't see me, until it's too late,
Because I am hiding. Isn't that great?

**HERO**
*(lifts up two paper footprints)*
I smell a rat and it doesn't smell sweet.
Footprints are here, but there are no feet.
I've nerves of steel and I shall be brave.
I'm not afraid, but — where is this Dave?

*The Giant steps out with a foam rubber bat and bops the Hero on the head, then drags him into the cave.*

# ACT II
## *The Giant's Cave*

*The cave is dimly lit. The Hero is inside a large cauldron.*

**GIANT**
Fee! I say, fie! And a fo fum and phooey!
Looks like I've caught something yummy and chewy.
He may be live, but soon he'll be dead.
Then I'll grind up his bones and make dead Hero bread!

**HERO**
How can this be? I've been popped in a pot.
If I am cooked, I won't like that a lot.

**CHORUS**
Our Hero is worried. He's very upset.
He shivers. He quivers. He breaks out in sweat.
Audience! Audience! Audience, please,
He needs some help. Say the magic word: CHEESE!

*When the audience shouts "Cheese!" the Mouse tiptoes out on the stage.*

**MOUSE**
Squeak. Did you call me? O giant named Dave,
This isn't a nice way for you to behave.

**GIANT**
Eek! It's a mouse. O, most foul brute!

**MOUSE**
Isn't that odd? I thought I was cute.

*The Giant backs away, frightened.*
*The Mouse chases him offstage.*

**HERO**

*(climbing out of the cauldron)*
Isn't it lucky that I was befriended?
Egads and gadzooks! The play might have ended.
There's no time to waste. I must find the Wizard.

**MOUSE**

Goodbye and good luck and —
watch out for the lizard!

*The Mouse skips offstage as the lights dim. As the*
*Hero speaks, the Dragon sneaks up behind him.*

**HERO**

I shall be brave — but it's black as the night.
I'm not afraid, but I wish it was light.

**DRAGON**

What's that you said? Did I hear the word light?
My fiery breath is both lovely and bright.

*The Dragon chases the Hero down through the*
*audience, then corners him back onstage.*

**HERO**

Egads! How disgraceful to go to my death,
Sizzled and fried in a lizard's bad breath.

**CHORUS**

Our Hero is worried. He's starting to fry.
He sizzles. He frizzles. Alas! He may die.
Audience! Audience! Audience, please.
He needs some help. Say the magic word :

**AUDIENCE**

CHEESE!

*The Mouse tiptoes out, carrying a water squirter.*

**MOUSE**

Squeak. Did you call me, O volcanic lizard?
A squirt of cold water should cool that hot gizzard.

*The Mouse squirts water into*
*the Dragon's mouth (or mouths).*

**CHORUS**

*(makes sizzling sounds)*

**DRAGON**

My head! My poor head! I've a cold in my head.
My fire is out, so I guess I am dead.

*Dragon stumbles around, then crumples to the floor.*

**MOUSE**

The Wizard awaits, and the maid in distress.
Watch out for the trap or you'll be in a mess.

*Storm effects: flashing lights, drums and cymbals.*

**HERO**

What's that I hear? Is that thunder and lightning?
I'm very brave . . . but . . . it is a bit frightening.

*The Wizard appears in a flash of lightning.*

**WIZARD**

There's no need to fear. I'm misunderstood!
See how I smile? I'm friendly. I'm good.

**HERO**

The Mouse was mistaken. He's not a bad chap.

*The Hero steps forward to shake his hand and is caught in an invisible net.*

**HERO**
Oh no! I have tripped in a terrible trap!
The Wizard has cast an invisible net.
This isn't funny. I'm very upset.

*The lights go out. The curtain closes.*

# ACT III
## *The Wizard's House*

*Inside the Wizard's house. The Princess is in chains. The Hero is sitting in a squished position, still caught in the invisible net. A large, mysterious-looking book is sitting on a table, along with a key. Somewhere else on stage is a magic wand.*

**WIZARD**
Ha ha! You're all mine! Ah, Princess, you'll be
Someone to love and to take care of me.

**PRINCESS**
That's what you think, but it's very untrue.
I couldn't love someone as rotten as you.

**WIZARD**
 *(exiting)*
I'll get the ring and we'll set the date.
Your Hero can't save you. Yes, I am your fate!

**CHORUS**
Our Hero is crying. He's down on his knees.
He's shaking. He's quaking. He's starting to wheeze.
Audience! Audience! Audience, please,
He needs your help. Say the magic word:

**AUDIENCE**
CHEESE!

**MOUSE**
*(appears, looking shocked)*
Squeak. Did you call me? Good gracious! I fear,
This could be the end of your Hero career!
With my sharp teeth, I shall bite through the net.
Don't cry, poor Hero. It's not over yet.

*The Mouse gnaws through the net and frees the Hero.*

**PRINCESS**
I'm still in these chains. Don't forget about me.
There isn't much time. Hand me that key!

*The Hero gets the key and unlocks the chain.*
*The Princess, freed, opens the Wizard's large book*
*and begins thumbing through it.*

**PRINCESS**
Now, go find his wand while I look for a spell.
Hmm. This one is nasty. Yes, this will do well.

*She mumbles to herself, memorizing. Meanwhile,*
*the Hero searches on stage and down in the*
*audience for the wand. Although the audience sees it*
*clearly, he keeps missing it. The audience may shout*
*encouragement and directions until he finds it.*

**HERO**
Aha! Here it is! Oh, I could grow fond,
Of swooshing around this wizardy wand.

*He waves the wand around. Lights flash as things,*
*and any number of new characters, appear out of*
*nowhere. Various sound effects are heard. Suddenly*
*the lights go off and all is quiet.*

**CHORUS**
Egads and gadzooks!
How the play's plot doth thicken.
He's bewitched the Princess and now —

*The lights go on again. The Princess is in a chicken*
*costume, the crown still on her head.*

**CHORUS**
She's a chicken!
Audience! Audience! Audience! Please,
She needs your help. Say the magic word:

**AUDIENCE**
CHEESE!

**MOUSE**
Squeak! Did you call me? What's happened? Oh dear.
Give me that wand. She needs fixing. That's clear.

*The Mouse waves the wand. The lights go off. When*
*they go on again, the Princess is her old self again.*

**PRINCESS**
Thank you. I thought I had run out of luck.
Imagine, a princess whose one word is "cluck"!
At last I am free. And before things get worse,
I'll take the wand and do my own verse.

*Takes the wand from the mouse.*

**PRINCESS**
Ssh! I hear footsteps. Get back in the net.

*The Princess winds the chain around her foot.*
*The Hero reluctantly gets back in the invisible net.*

**WIZARD**
*(offstage)*
Princess. Oh, Princess. Where are you, my pet?

**PRINCESS**
Right where you left me. Come here, Wizard dear.
I have a secret I'd like you to hear.

*The Wizard enters with a large diamond ring. He closes his eyes and cups his ear to listen. The Princess leans toward him, the wand behind her back.*

**PRINCESS**
Oodle noodle. Kit kaboodle.
Sweetie pie, my own.

*She brings the wand forward and taps him on the head.*

**PRINCESS**
Toodle-oodle, apple strudel,
Now you're turned to stone.

*The Wizard freezes in his position. The other characters on stage dance joyously around him. The curtain closes.*

**CF**
Th_ _nd. There will be no more hassle.
Th_ _ _ the statue back to the castle.

*The Hero steps out in front of the curtain and bows.*

**HERO**
The Princess is safe. The Queen is delighted.
And for my trouble, I shall be knighted.

*The Princess steps out in front of the curtain and curtsies*

**PRINCESS**
Come on, everybody, back to my house.
It's time for my wedding. I'll marry —

*The Hero smiles and swaggers, as the Princess reaches through the closed curtains and brings forth the Mouse.*

**PRINCESS**
. . . The Mouse!!!

*The Mouse bows and reaches through the curtains, bringing forth the rest of the cast single file. When they are all assembled they bow in unison.*

The End